j811　**Service, Robert W illiam, 1874-1958**
S　　　　The shooting of Dan McGrew [and] The cremation of Sam
　　　McGee. Illus. by Rosemary Wells. Designed by Susan Jeffers.
　　　Scott, W. R., c1969.
　　　　　unp.　illus.　　　　　4.25
　　　　Two humorous poems depicting the rough life of the turn
　　　of the century Canadian Yukon.

　　　　1. Yukon territory — Poetry.　I. Title.　II. Title: The
　　　cremation of Sam McGee.
　　　　　　　　　57690Ap70

B 31-796
LJ Cards © 1969

23　　　811
　　　—j

THE
SHOOTING
OF
DAN McGREW

THE
CREMATION
OF
SAM McGEE

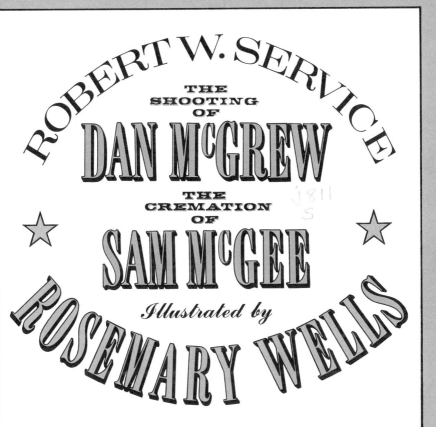

ROBERT W. SERVICE

THE
SHOOTING
OF
DAN McGREW

THE
CREMATION
OF
SAM McGEE

Illustrated by

ROSEMARY WELLS

DESIGNED BY SUSAN JEFFERS

Young Scott Books

FOR AVA

THE SHOOTING OF DAN McGREW

A bunch of the boys were whooping it up
    in the Malamute Saloon;
The kid that handles the music box
    was hitting a jag-time tune;
Back of the bar, in a solo game,
    sat Dangerous Dan McGrew,
And watching his luck was his light-o'-love,
    the lady that's known as Lou.

When out of the night, which was fifty below,
    and into the din and the glare,
There stumbled a miner fresh from the creeks,
    dog-dirty, and loaded for bear.
He looked like a man with a foot in the grave
    and scarcely the strength of a louse,

Yet he tilted a poke of dust on the bar,
    and he called for drinks for the house.
There was none could place the stranger's face,
    though we searched ourselves for a clue;
But we drank his health, and the last to drink
    was Dangerous Dan McGrew.

There's men that somehow just grip your eyes,
    and hold them hard like a spell;
And such was he, and he looked to me
    like a man who had lived in hell;
With a face most hair, and a dreary stare
    of a dog whose day is done,
As he watered the green stuff in his glass,
    and the drops fell one by one.
Then I got to figgering who he was,
    and wondering what he'd do,
And I turned my head—and there watching him
    was the lady that's known as Lou.

His eyes went rubbering round the room,
        and he seemed in a kind of daze,
Till at last that old piano fell in the way
        of his wandering gaze.
The rag-time kid was having a drink;
        there was no one else on the stool,
So the stranger stumbles across the room,
        and flops down there like a fool.
In a buckskin shirt that was glazed with dirt
        he sat, and I saw him sway;
Then he clutched the keys with his talon hands—
        my God! but that man could play.

Were you ever out in the Great Alone,
     when the moon was awful clear,
And the icy mountains hemmed you in
     with a silence you most could *hear;*
With only the howl of a timber wolf,
     and you camped there in the cold,
A half-dead thing in a stark, dead world,
     clean mad for the muck called gold;
While high overhead, green, yellow and red,
     the North Lights swept in bars?—
Then you've a hunch what the music meant . . .
     hunger and night and the stars.

And hunger not of the belly kind,
    that's banished with bacon and beans,
But the gnawing hunger of lonely men
    for a home and all that it means;
For a fireside far from the cares that are,
    four walls and a roof above;
But oh! so cramful of cosy joy,
    and crowned with a woman's love—
A woman dearer than all the world,
    and true as Heaven is true—
(God! how ghastly she looks through her rouge,—
    the lady that's known as Lou.)

Then on a sudden the music changed,
    so soft that you scarce could hear;
But you felt that your life had been looted clean
    of all that it once held dear;
That someone had stolen the woman you loved;
    that her love was a devil's lie;
That your guts were gone, and the best for you
    was to crawl away and die.
'Twas the crowning cry of a heart's despair,
    and it thrilled you through and through—
"I guess I'll make it a spread misere,"
    said Dangerous Dan McGrew.

The music almost died away . . .
    then it burst like a pent-up flood;
And it seemed to say, "Repay, repay,"
    and my eyes were blind with blood.
The thought came back of an ancient wrong,
    and it stung like a frozen lash,
And the lust awoke to kill, to kill . . .
    then the music stopped with a crash,
And the stranger turned, and his eyes they burned
    in a most peculiar way;
In a buckskin shirt that was glazed with dirt
    he sat, and I saw him sway;
Then his lips went in in a kind of grin,
    and he spoke, and his voice was calm,
And "Boys," says he, "you don't know me,
    and none of you care a damn;
But I want to state, and my words are straight,
    and I'll bet my poke they're true,
That one of you is a hound of hell . . .
    and that one is Dan McGrew."

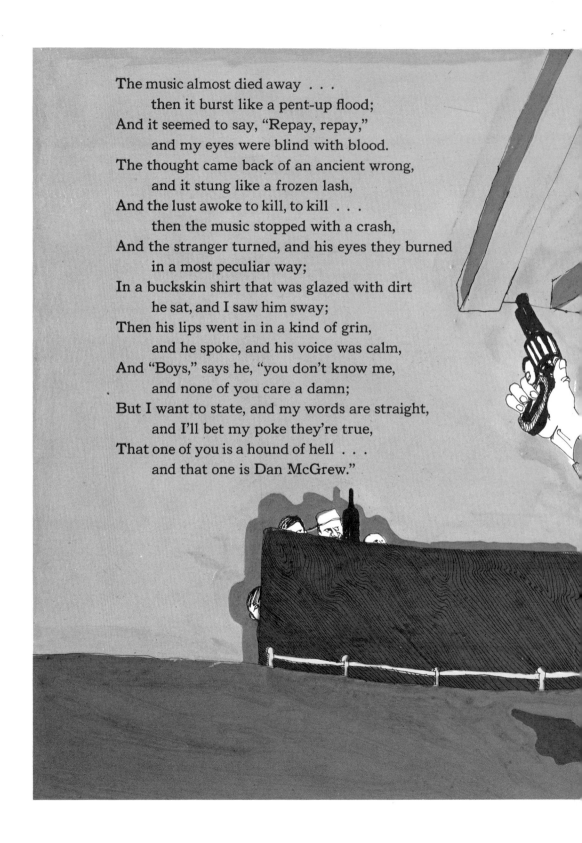

Then I ducked my head, and the lights went out,
and two guns blazed in the dark,
And a woman screamed, and the lights went up,
and two men lay stiff and stark.

Pitched on his head, and pumped full of lead,
    was Dangerous Dan McGrew.
While the man from the creeks lay clutched to the breast
    of the lady that's known as Lou.

These are the simple facts of the case,
    and I guess I ought to know.
They say the stranger was crazed with "hooch,"
    and I'm not denying it's so.
I'm not so wise as the lawyer guys,
    but strictly between us two—

The woman that kissed him and—pinched his poke—
was the lady that's known as Lou.

There are strange things done in the midnight sun
    By the men who moil for gold;
The Arctic trails have their secret tales
    That would make your blood run cold;
The Northern Lights have seen queer sights,
    But the queerest they ever did see
Was that night on the marge of Lake Lebarge
    I cremated Sam McGee.

Now Sam McGee was from Tennessee,
    where the cotton blooms and blows.
Why he left his home in the South to roam
    'round the Pole, God only knows.
He was always cold, but the land of gold
    seemed to hold him like a spell;
Though he'd often say in his homely way
    that "he'd sooner live in hell."

On a Christmas Day we were mushing our way
      over the Dawson trail.
Talk of your cold! through the parka's fold
      it stabbed like a driven nail.
If our eyes we'd close, then our lashes froze
      till sometimes we couldn't see;
It wasn't much fun, but the only one
      to whimper was Sam McGee.

And that very night, as we lay packed tight
    in our robes beneath the snow,
And the dogs were fed, and the stars o'erhead
    were dancing heel and toe,
He turned to me, and "Cap," says he,
    "I'll cash in this trip, I guess;
And if I do, I'm asking that you
    won't refuse my last request."

Well, he seemed so low that I couldn't say no;
    then he says with a sort of a moan:
"It's the cursed cold, and it's got right hold
    till I'm chilled clean through to the bone.
Yet 'tain't being dead—it's my awful dread
    of the icy grave that pains;
So I want you to swear that, foul or fair,
    you'll cremate my last remains."

A pal's last need is a thing to heed,
 so I swore I would not fail;
And we started on at the streak of dawn,
 but God! he looked ghastly pale.
He crouched on the sleigh and he raved all day
 of his home in Tennessee;
And before nightfall a corpse was all
 that was left of Sam McGee.

There wasn't a breath in that land of death,
 and I hurried, horror-driven,
With a corpse half hid that I couldn't get rid,
 because of a promise given;
It was lashed to the sleigh, and it seemed to say:
 "You may tax your brawn and brains,
But you promised true, and it's up to you
 to cremate those last remains."

Now a promise made is a debt unpaid,
    and the trail has its own stern code.
In the days to come, though my lips were dumb,
    in my heart how I cursed that load.
In the long, long night, by the lone firelight,
    while the huskies, round in a ring,
Howled out their woes to the homeless snows—
    O God! how I loathed the thing.

And every day that quiet clay
        seemed to heavy and heavier grow;
And on I went, though the dogs were spent
        and the grub was getting low;
The trail was bad, and I felt half mad,
        but I swore I would not give in;
And I'd often sing to the hateful thing,
        and it hearkened with a grin.

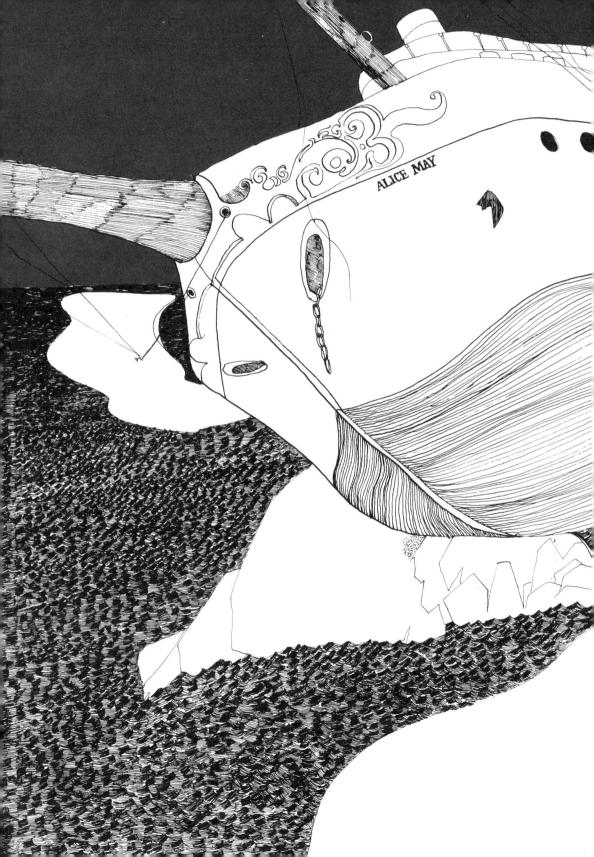

Till I came to the marge of Lake Lebarge,
    and a derelict there lay;
It was jammed in the ice, but I saw in a trice
    it was called the "Alice May."
And I looked at it, and I thought a bit,
    and I looked at my frozen chum;
Then "Here," said I, with a sudden cry,
    "is my cre-ma-tor-eum."

Some planks I tore from the cabin floor,
    and I lit the boiler fire;
Some coal I found that was lying around,
    and I heaped the fuel higher;
The flames just soared, and the furnace roared—
    such a blaze you seldom see;
And I burrowed a hole in the glowing coal,
    and I stuffed in Sam McGee.

Then I made a hike, for I didn't like
 to hear him sizzle so;
And the heavens scowled, and the huskies howled,
 and the wind began to blow.
It was icy cold, but the hot sweat rolled
 down my cheeks, and I don't know why;
And the greasy smoke in an inky cloak
 went streaking down the sky.

 I do not know how long in the snow
 I wrestled with grisly fear;
But the stars came out and they danced about
 ere again I ventured near;

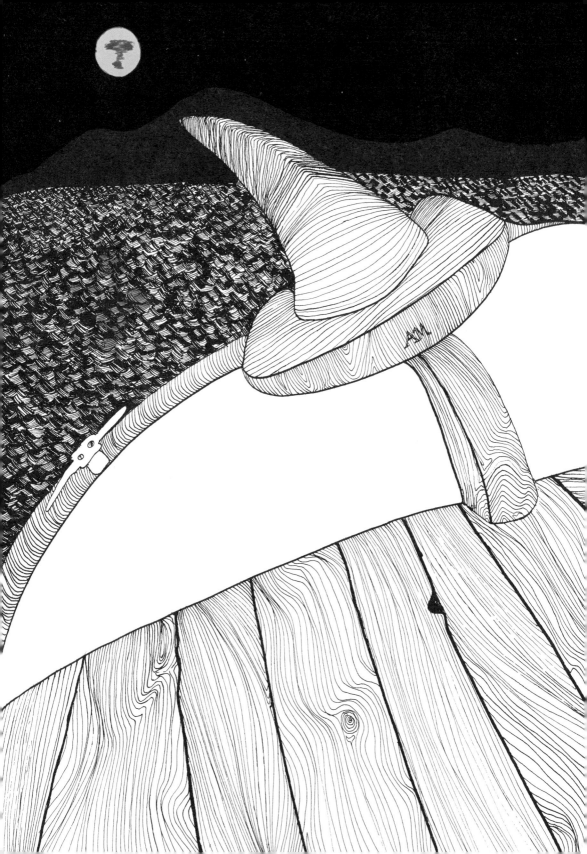

I was sick with dread, but I bravely said:
     "I'll just take a peep inside.
I guess he's cooked and it's time I looked". . .
     then the door I opened wide.

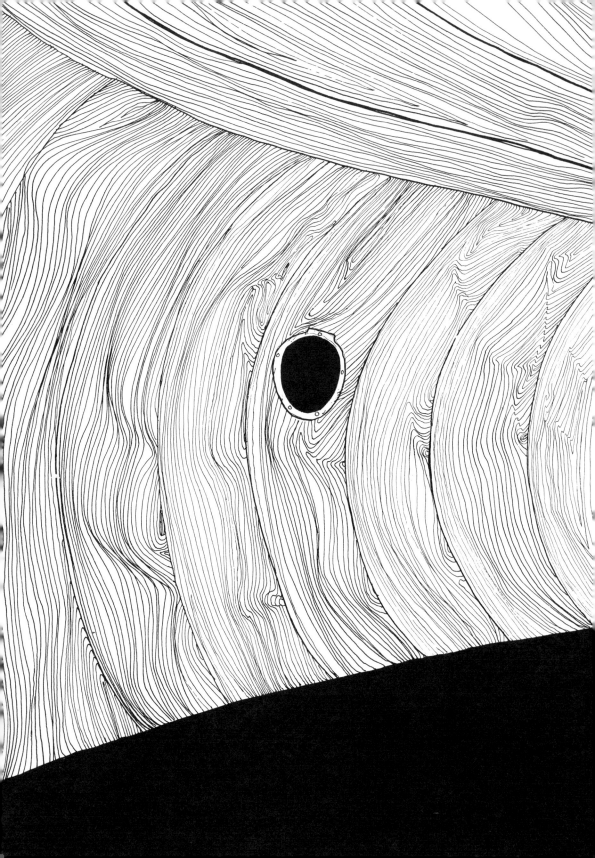

And there sat Sam, looking cool and calm,
    in the heart of the furnace roar;
And he wore a smile you could see a mile,
    and he said: "Please close that door.
It's fine in here, but I greatly fear
    you'll let in the cold and storm—

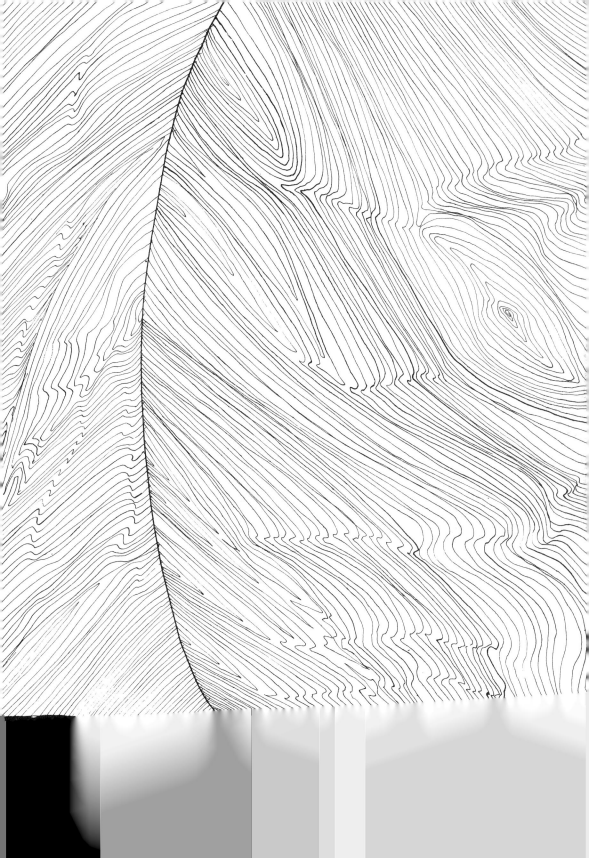

There are strange things done in the midnight sun
    By the men who moil for gold;
The Arctic trails have their secret tales
    That would make your blood run cold;
The Northern Lights have seen queer sights,
    But the queerest they ever did see
Was that night on the marge of Lake Lebarge
    I cremated Sam McGee.

ABOUT THE POET

Born in England in 1874, Robert W. Service grew up in Scotland where he attended high school. After he graduated, he became apprenticed as a bank clerk, but this proved to be much too dull a job for a young man with his abundant energy and imagination.

In 1888 he emigrated to western Canada and for ten years traveled up and down the Pacific coast from British Columbia to Los Angeles working at a variety of jobs and at the same time writing poetry. In 1905, he took a job as a teller in a Canadian bank and he was soon transferred to branches at Whitehorse and Dawson in the Yukon. It was here that Service began to turn out vivid ballads depicting life in the frozen north where hunters, trappers, gold prospectors and other adventurers flourished.

His poems first appeared in a collection called *Songs of a Sourdough* in 1907. This book made him famous. After three more years in the north, he left Canada to serve as a war correspondent for the *Toronto Star* in the Balkans.

In 1913 he married a French girl whom he met in a train wreck in France. He served in the First World War as an ambulance driver and intelligence officer with the Canadian Army. After the war was over, he and his wife settled down in France.

Although Service continued to write until his death in 1958, nothing he later wrote approached the vigor and originality of his first poems about the Yukon.